BARKING

BATSHIT

BANANAS

BARMY

NATTERS

TOUCHED

SCREW LOOSE

TAPPED

NUTS

CUCKOO

NOT RIGHT UP TOP

OO LALLY

LOO

FOR STEPHEN

FRUITCAKE

BONKERS

CRACKERS

LO

STARK RAVING

OON

OFF YOUR ROCKE

BARKING

Lucy Sullivan

1

TS

KO

E PLOT

FOREWORD

The story you're about to read had a long gestation and is the result of years of creative percolation. I know this because I know how long Lucy's been thinking about making this story happen.

It's a big thing – creating something out of nothing; a new and original cultural artefact that didn't previously exist except as inchoate notions. In the age of the Internet, when we all routinely get content for free and create it every day, through social media for the consumption of others, it doesn't really seem like that big of a deal.

Only, all content – all stories – are born from experience, and life experience always exacts a price. Storytelling isn't digital gossip or conversation or dot-joining or layered commentary. A lot of people think comics come out of the end of a pen; that you draw the pictures, add some speech balloons, throw some words in them and it all sort of glues itself together. Well, that can happen, but truth is, comics is about as sophisticated a language and storytelling medium as you'll find.

When I first met Lucy, she came to a signing I did when I was promoting my 2007 graphic novel *Laika*. The first question out of her mouth was something like, "How did you do it?"

How does anyone make something that people remember?

By a weird coincidence, a few years later she became my life drawing teacher when she took over the classes I attended at Kingston University. We drew a lot, became good friends, and we batted that same question about over a period of years.

Truth is, there's no one easy answer. Making a comic, a graphic narrative of any kind (especially if you're writing and drawing it) takes a peculiar kind of dedication and commitment. It's a big thing to take on, to create something out of nothing – some would say, in an age when stories come and go, thick and fast, and few stick in the memory, that it's a Sisyphean task. The book you're reading here is drawn from Lucy's own life experience, as all the most memorable stories are, itself an act of creative courage beyond the decision to just sit down and make something. Beyond taking the time to shape the story and invest it with that emotional truth, I know that Lucy sweated over every line and detail.

It's a testament to Lucy's determination, talent and skill that you now hold this book in your hands; that the story of creating it has already had the kind of impact it's had online. What you see on the page is not content, not gossip, not anecdotal art therapy. Lucy will play down what went into it, but I know.

It's a performance, a lifetime in the making, and straight from the heart. Cheer for her.

— Nick Abadzis, New York, 2019

1. Hounded

OCTOBER 25TH 4:45PM

2. COMMIT TO ME

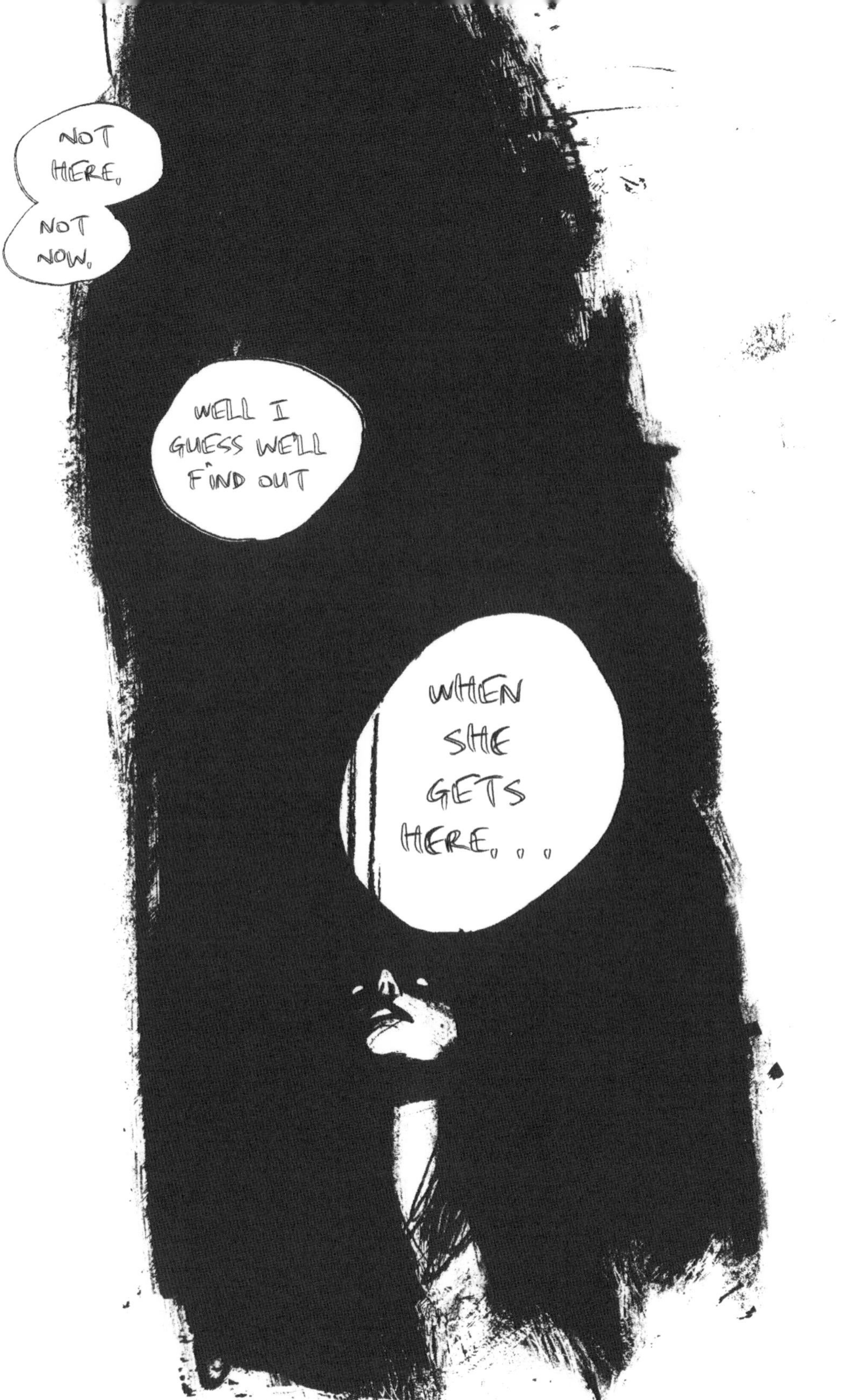
NOT HERE.
NOT NOW.
WELL I GUESS WE'LL FIND OUT
WHEN SHE GETS HERE...

3. ROT BOX

OCTOBER 25TH 6:45PM
SHE'S ON SEVENTY TWO.
YOU TAKE FIRST SPECIAL.
B.P.D MEDIUM TO MILD RISK.
BUT DOESN'T SEEM UP TO MUCH SO FAR...
BAZ
WHAT DOES THAT MEAN?
!!SPECIAL!
CHEEKY COW.

SHE ALWAYS FOUND COMPANY,

I NEEDED SPACE!

SHE JUST WAS SUFFOCATING.

OR IT FOUND HER,

FOR A LITTLE WHILE

AT LEAST,

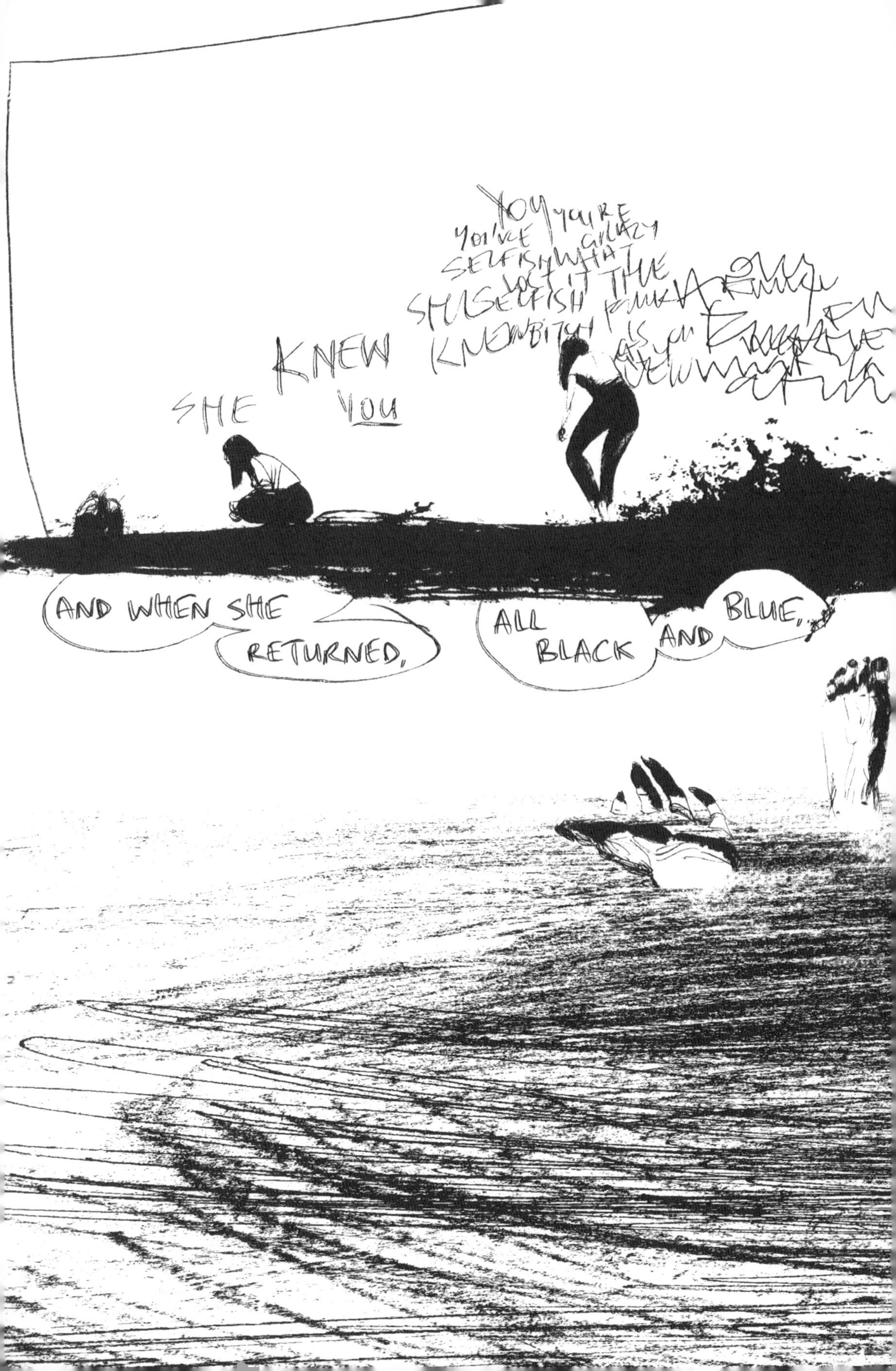
SHE
KNEW
YOU
AND WHEN SHE RETURNED,
ALL BLACK AND BLUE,

4. PRONE TO TROUBLE

OCTOBER 25TH 9:15PM

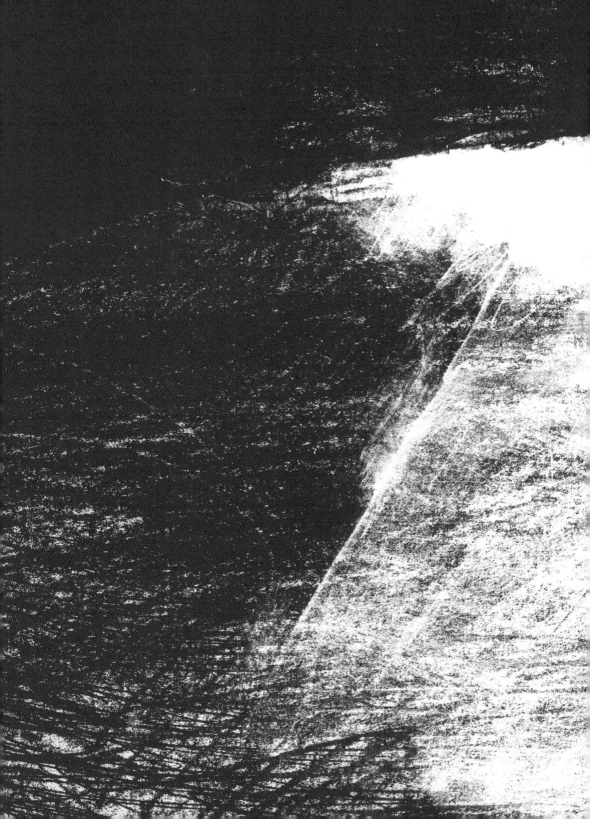

5. JUST A (RUMINATION) PHASE

6. UNEMBODIED DIAMONIC

TODAY WE'RE GOING TO TRY TO STOP...

FORTUNE-TELLING AND OVER GENERALISATION.

YOU'LL HAVE TO PLAY CATCH UP, MISS OTTO.

SO...TODAY I MISSED THE BUS BECAUSE... I HAVE BAD LUCK? DID I MISS IT BECAUSE ONLY BAD THINGS HAPPEN TO ME, GROUP? NO INDEED! I MISSED IT BECAUSE MY HUSBAND CAN'T FIND HIS KEYS! HA HA HA SILLY MAN.

FILL IT OUT AND BE HONEST, MISS OTTO.

IT'S ALIX

SUSAN?

ANY STRANGE VISITORS?

NO, MUCH BETTER. THANK YOU, NURSE OMIATA.

SEE

I KNOW NOW THEY CANNOT REALY HURT ME.

FIRE

THEY ARE NO WE CAN

YES WE CAN SUSAN

I M A

IT'S THE ONLY WAY TO GET BETTER.

COME, MEET LOZZA.

I'M DORATHEA, BUT EVERYONE CALLS ME DOLLY.

DOLLY HORROR!

DON'T MIND LOZZA SHE HAS THE SIGHT. BUT A BIG MOUTH TOO.

MAKES FOR TENSE INTRO'S.

ALRIGHT? COME LOWER...

IT'S READY.

WHAT DOES YOUR FEELING SAY TO YOU?
YOU ARE A WASTE

WHY DO YOU FEEL THIS WAY?
BECAUSE IT'S TRUE

CAN YOU MAKE THE SITUATION THAT MADE YOU FEEL THIS WAY A POSITIVE ONE? HOW DOES THAT CHANGE YOUR FEELING? MAYBE THE SAME.

9. BRUISING THE FOOL

EVERYONE FORGETS,
ONCE YOU'RE DEAD...
YOU'RE AN INNOCENT.

NO MATTER
HOW CRAP A
HUMAN YOU
MIGHT'VE BEEN.

SHE WALKED ABOUT
IN MY SKIN
THEN SAID IT WASN'T
GOOD ENOUGH.

I WANTED
TO
GET AWAY.

I WANTED
OUT
FROM... HER.

SHE SHOULD'VE GONE... FOR GOOD.
INSTEAD SHE FESTERED IN ME.
I CAN'T SHAKE HER.

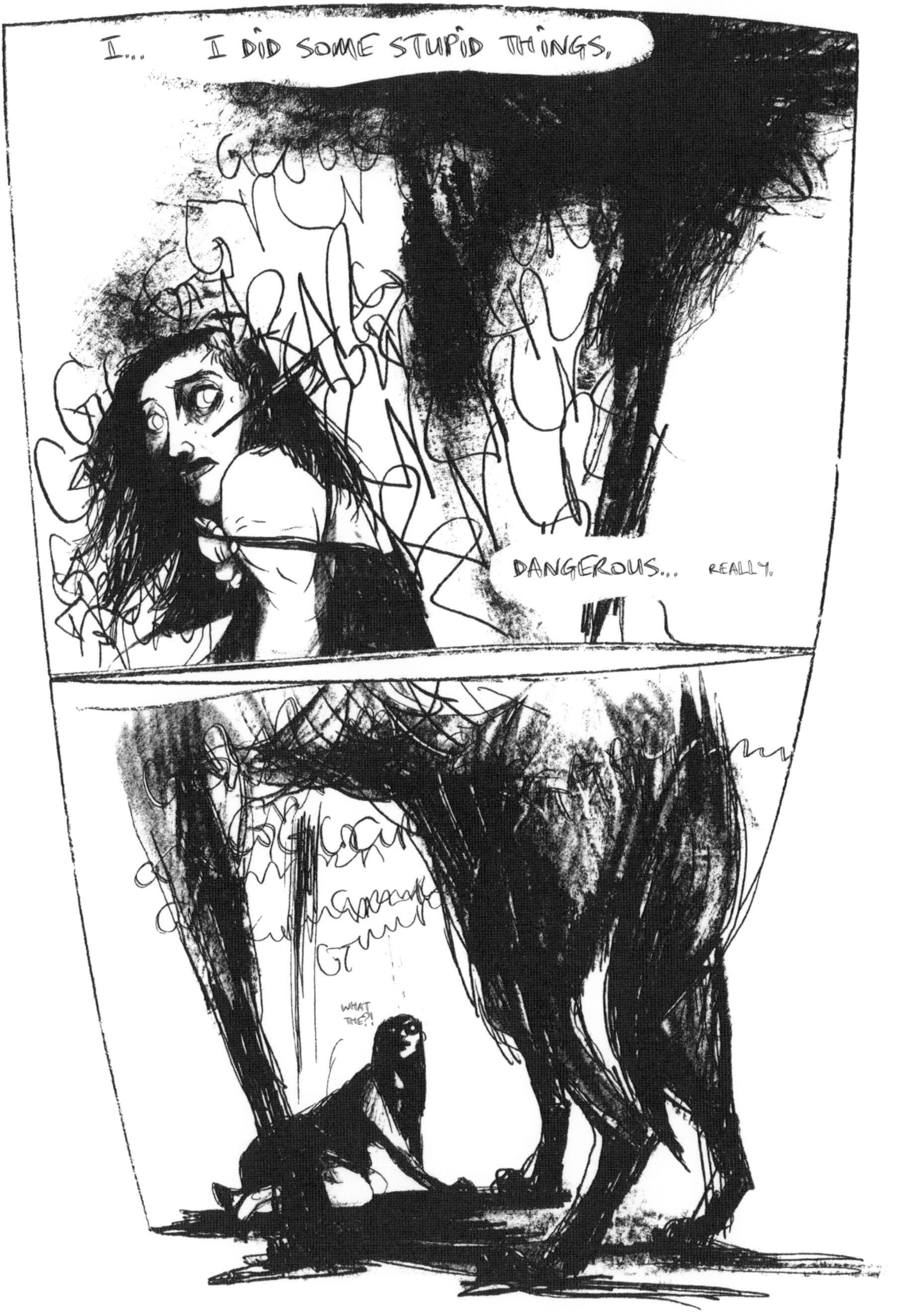
I... I DID SOME STUPID THINGS.
DANGEROUS... REALLY.
WHAT THE?!

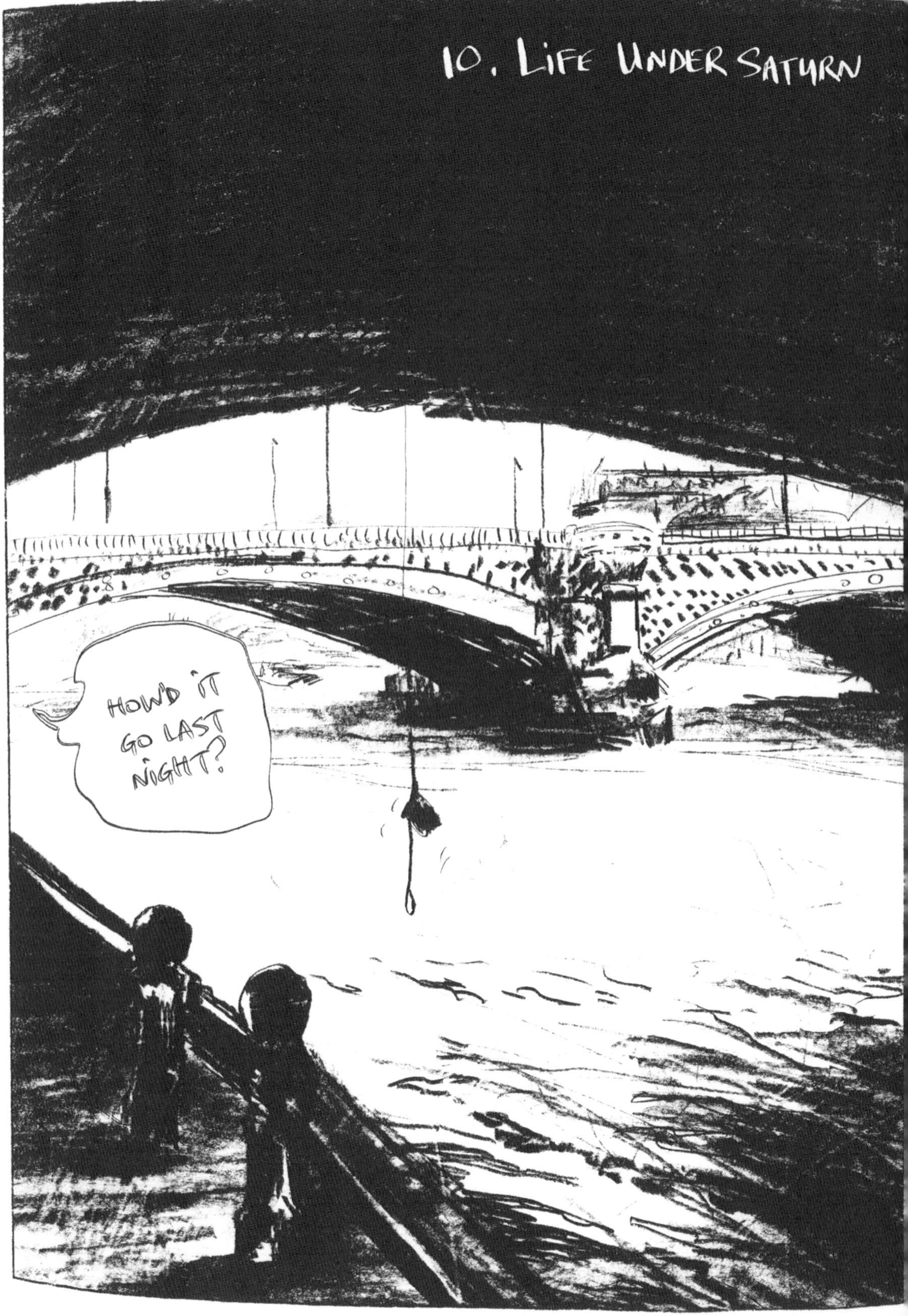
10. Life Under Saturn
HOW'D IT GO LAST NIGHT?

November 5th 4:45pm

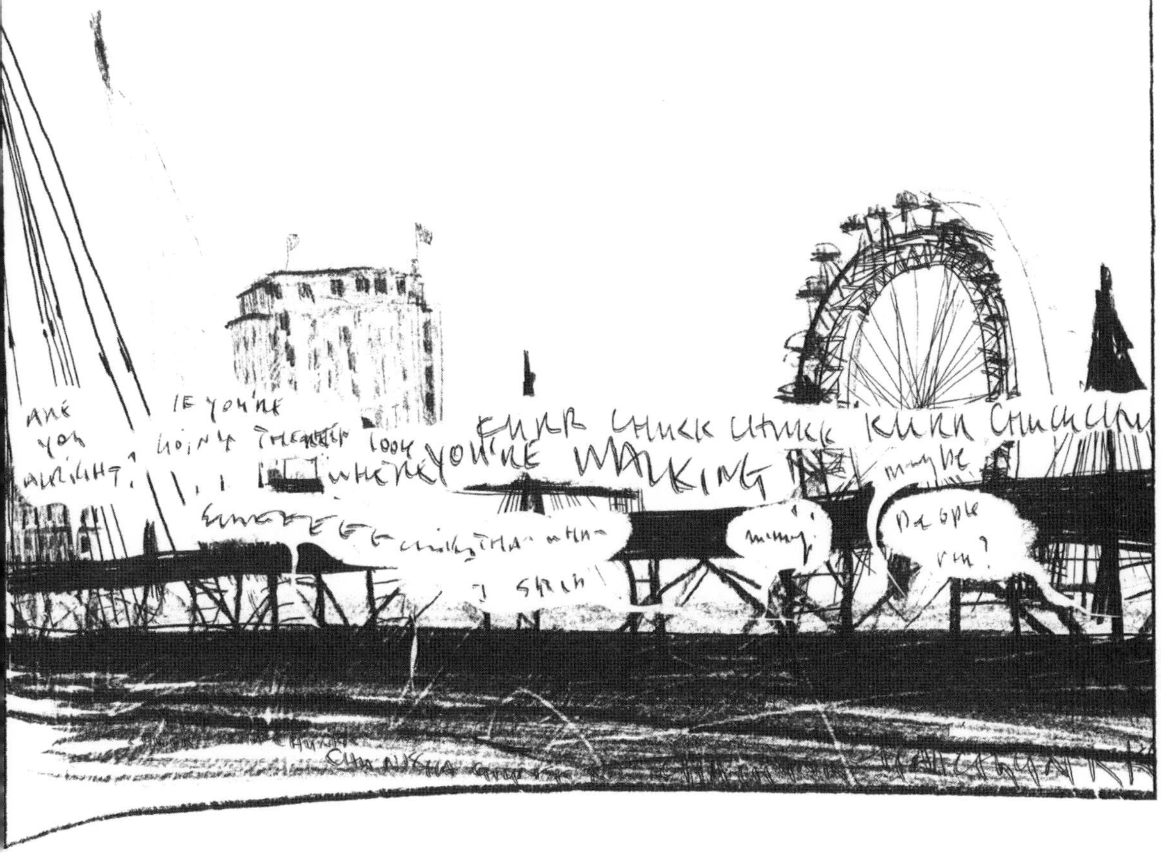
ARE YOU ALRIGHT?
LOOK WHERE YOU'RE WALKING

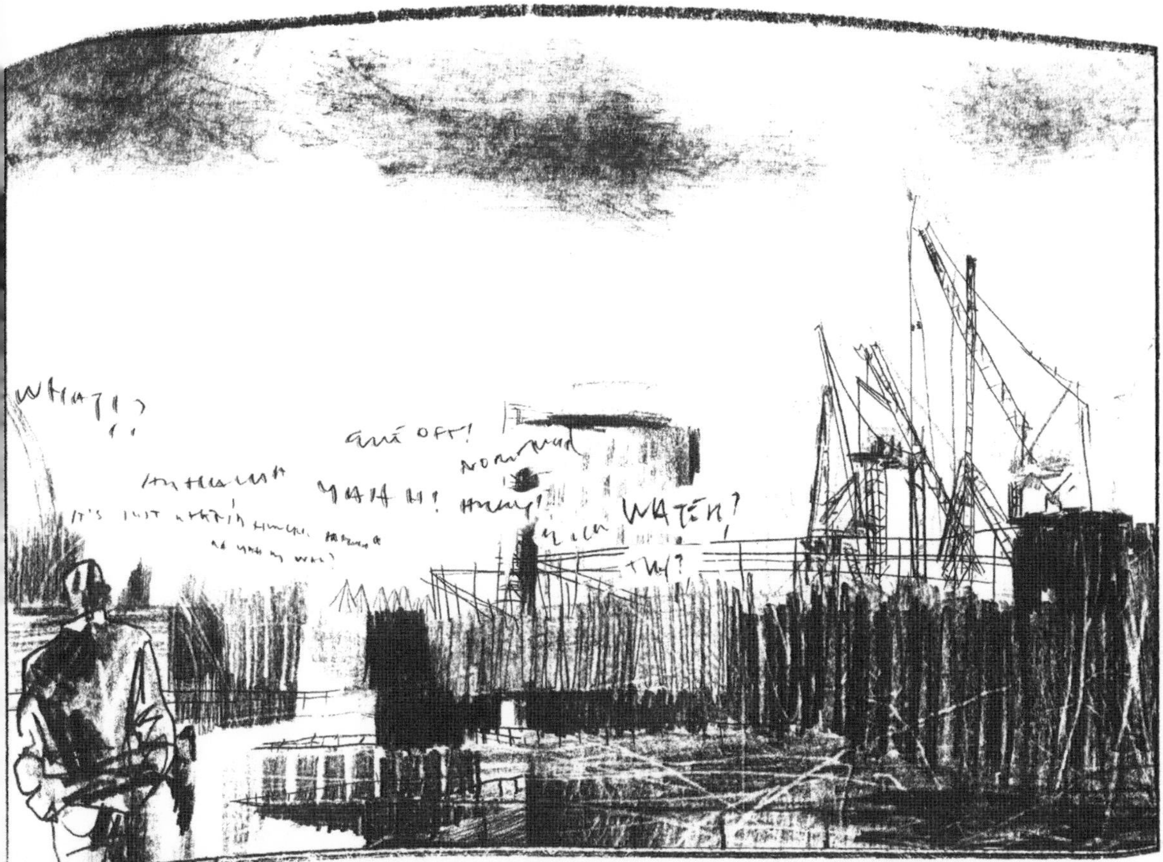
WHAT!?
GET OFF!
WATER?

AFTERWORD

This book is an allegory born out of my own experience, those of my friends, and my research into mental health crises. There is such a wealth of things to talk about when it comes to mental illness and how we, as a society, view and treat those in the grip of a terrifying experience, and ultimately at a vulnerable point in their lives. Most of what is in this story is based on lived events. To be honest, I had to tone some of them down to make them easier to take on board if you have never had this happen to you, or stepped foot in a psychiatric ward.

Personally, despite a deep respect for the NHS and its staff, I disagree with a system that reduces the complexity of the mind, and the ways it can crack, to treatment under one umbrella approach. It's a system that places people who are a danger to themselves and those who are a danger to others in one confined, stressful environment. Everyone – the patients, the staff and the visitors – within those wards then brings their own individual social conditioning into the mix and you can see how easily the waters get muddied. There is no question for me that the situation has to change.

I can't offer a solution but I can talk about what it can be like for a person swallowed up by it all. I'm not alone in this, either. In making this book I have connected with other comic creators, writers, artists and mental health advocates who are all doing their upmost to highlight a subject that remains not only taboo, but woefully misunderstood.

I was confronted with my mental health when I was twenty-three. I was living in New Zealand when my dad died suddenly of a brain aneurysm. The subsequent flights home to London and the abrupt adjustment to being back there left me utterly broken. I was lucky that my grief was only about the loss and shock of my dad's death. Death can be more complicated than this, but for me the complications were with the living. Grief brings many expectations. Of who will arrange what, take over which and look after whom. Much is left undiscussed and as such can lead to miscommunication and resentment. My mum and dad were publicans who ran well-known and very popular pubs and events. These were raucous, boozy and fun-filled for the displaced Australasian communities in London. We had a large family of bar staff, bouncers and regulars so that when Dad died his loss was felt deeply by many. It's easy in those situations for everyone to slip into their personal grief, and we all did. I internalised mine, which festered within me, and around a year or so later I found that I couldn't contain the scrawling mess I had become inside. My anger was enveloping me, becoming focused but misdirected at everyone and everything. I was trying to cling onto who I was before, but finding instead a stranger. Trying to be a twenty-something full of life, but finding I was bitter, resentful and out of step with my peer group. A few people broke through my barriers. I'm forever grateful to those that maintained empathy, the new friends that saw past the cracked version of myself and the ones that told me without gloss that I had an anger problem. Because problems can be fixed. It was easy in the face of my constant aggression to write it off as who I was now. But it wasn't and isn't who I am. I am merely the person to whom it happened.

I was fortunate not to be sectioned, and sought help privately. In the years that followed I saw a number of friends who were not so lucky. My anger and frustration at how they were treated grew until it became a drive to push these confusing and dehumanising experiences into this graphic novel and hopefully start a broader conversation around mental illness. If you are fortunate enough not have mental health problems then I hope this story will aid you in considering how you would cope if your world collapsed. If one in four people will suffer a mental health crisis in their lives, then it could be you, or someone you love. I hope if that does happen you are treated with the compassion and dignity we all deserve. Because there is no 'crazy'. There are just different ways of seeing the world. Be kind to others and to yourself, and if you think you can't cope, go and talk to someone. Talk to whomever you feel comfortable with: it may surprise you who can help. Just telling someone, anyone, will make it easier.

Thank you for reading.

— Lucy Sullivan, London, 2019

ACKNOWLEDGEMENTS

This book was supported by public funding from the National Lottery through Arts Council England and the Lakes International Comic Art Festival. Thank you for supporting and contributing to this project – it's a crucial step in helping to raise awareness of mental health issues.

A special shout out to the UK small press and worldwide comics communities, who have welcomed me and embraced this project in a way that was totally unexpected and wonderfully uplifting. I'm still stunned by how many of you generously backed this book and brought so many more readers to the project. I'm genuinely honoured to have your support.

My fellow Unbound authors, who take the plunge and embark on the epic journey of crowdfunding a literary work. I'm thrilled to be in such talented company.

Jeff Lemire, who supported the book early on, promoted it widely and took time out of his ludicrously busy schedule to write a cover quote. Thank you so much!

Massive thanks to Dan Berry for creating a brilliant font just for this project that is so close to my handwriting even I couldn't tell the difference. You are truly a Renaissance man.

James Trevelyan of Arts Council England and Nicola Streeten of Laydeez Do Comics, whose input and advice were pivotal in gaining my funding grant.

A very enthusiastic thumbs up for social media through which I've connected with and met an extraordinary range of people, many of whom helped to bring this book to print. It's been inspirational, enlightening and gloriously frivolous chatting with you all.

There are so many people to thank for supporting me and this project, many of whom are listed here in my amazing supporters list. I'm overwhelmed by the talent and gravitas reflected in that list and very proud to have you all on board. It has taken over a decade to bring this project to life, so to all my family, friends, students, colleagues, fellow comic creators, zinesters, artists, podcasters, writers, journalists, comic shops and social media pals my heartfelt gratitude is endless.

This project would have died in the water if it weren't for the tireless and unswerving belief in me that my partner Stephen has. I love you very much and I'm so grateful for all the sacrifices you've made and the support you've given me throughout the years. Not to mention lettering this book in its entirety when I was drowning under my workload. Thank you, I couldn't have done any of this without you.

To my daughter Frankie, I'm sorry I had to miss so many adventures to get my book made. I hope you can forgive me and that this story may be of help to you one day too. With any luck your effervescent nature will keep the black clouds at bay.

Thanks to my mum Jean and sister Clair for their support and help with the day-to-day obstacles of freelancing while raising a family. I hope nothing you read here shocks you. We fought our individual demons after that day and I think we are a stronger family for it.

To my dad, Sean. Still the most unique, silliest and greatest of dads. I miss him as much today as that horrific day twenty years ago, but I know that without that happening the friends I've made, the life I've built and the love I've found may not have happened either. Or even this book for that matter. I'm sure he'd be proud as punch of it all.

Finally, to my good friends: Nick Abadzis, who encouraged me to make this comic and took me to a party that changed my path as an artist forever, and his wonderful words. Pedro Serrazina and Natalie Woolf who gifted the animation paper that this book was drawn on. And Lizzie Kaye, my editor at Unbound, whose great empathy for the subject and belief in the project brought it to life even when I foolishly tried to talk her out of it. I will be forever grateful for all of your support.

Unbound is the world's first crowdfunding publisher, established in 2011.

We believe that wonderful things can happen when you clear a path for people who share a passion. That's why we've built a platform that brings together readers and authors to crowdfund books they believe in – and give fresh ideas that don't fit the traditional mould the chance they deserve. This book is in your hands because readers made it possible.

Everyone who pledged their support is listed below. Join them by visiting unbound.com and supporting a book todaay.

Tom Abba
Stafforini Aixa
Eli Allison
Lulu Allison
Bonnie Alvarado
Sophie Ambrose
Kate Anderson
Rima Sabina Aouf
Christine Asbury
Richard Ashcroft
Mariel Ashlinn Kelly
Mitra Assadpour
Katerina Athanasopoulou
Liz Atkin
Camille Aubry
James Baldwin
Adam Bancroft
Hannah Berry
Dean Beswick
Tim Bird
Alister Black
Shi Blank
Shelly Bond
Ryan Bonder
Harriet Booth
Celine Bopp

Mark Bowsher
Martina Bramkamp
Suzi Bratt
Cathy Brett
Daniel Bristow-Bailey
Peter Brown
Stephen Bruce
Nick Bryan
Justinian Bucckley
Louisa Buck
Erica Buist
Emma Burleigh
Lazlo Burns
John Callaghan
Lara Callaghan
Cecile Campagne
Fraser Campbell
Barbara Chamberlin
Fiona Chapman
Gami Chou
Sue Clark
Jonathan Clode
Joanna Conrad
Emma Cook
Greg Cook
Adam Cooper

Annabel Cox
Eleanor Crewes
Cliff Cumber
Kim Curtin
Ryan Davies
Stephanie Davies
Rob Davis
Paul Dawes
Igor De Baecke
Claire Dean
Jan Dean
Rich Dodgin
Remembering Calum
   Downes
Clair Draper
Dulwich Art Group
D Duong
Christine Eade
Wallis Eates
Daniel Eckhart
Tracey Eva Edwards
Tat Effby
Monica-Niki Elenbaas
Daniel Elkin
Sophie Ell
Emporium Purgatorio

Josh More
Peter Morey
Mundy Morn
James Murray
Charity Musasa
Rhel ná DecVandé
Peter Nagle
Rana Nasser
Carlo Navato
Julia Naves
Amanda Nercessian
Emily Nevitt
Marie Nicholson
Lasse Nielsen
Duncan Nimmo
Matthew Noe
Emily Oliver
Emily Owen
Ana Padilla
Page 45
James Craig Paterson
Esme Pears
Paul Peart-Smith
Craig Perry
Norman Picken
Daniel Poitras
Justin Pollard
Jane Porter
Erika Price
Tina Price-Johnson
Maureen Putland
Elizabeth Querstret
Sarah Raybould
Anna Readman
Crash Reynolds
Mark Rider

Katya Riley
Liam Riley
John Riordan
Josh Roberts
Megan Roberts
Jennifer Robins
Holly, Daisy and John
    Rogers-McGrath
Matt Rogerson
Kate Rolison
Christine Rolph
Matt Rothwell
Simon Russell
Michael Safranek
Robert Sanders
Sam Savage
Niklas Schütze
Jodi Shadforth
Clare Sharp
Heather Sherratt
Matthew Shiell
Dean Simons
Alan Sims
Emma Smith
Stephanie Kay Smith
Nick Sousanis
Dorry Spikes
Anouska Stahlmann
Chloe Starling
Heather Steed
Ben Will Stirk
Joe Stone
Shelley Stonehouse
Merlin Strangeway
Nicola Streeten
Clair Sullivan

David Taylor
Brian Thompson
Steve Thompson
William Todd-Jones
Marcus Tolan
Alex Tomlinson
Myfanwy Tristram
Uncomfortable Revolution
Amandeep Uppal
Nuria Vakil
The Valkyries
Tony Vanderheyden
Ram Venkatesan
Ellie Warren
Lulu Warren & Robert Koot
Harriet Webster
Robert Wells
David White
Lyndon White
Nick White
Ian Williams
Samuel Williams
Luke Wilmot
Laura Wood
Tom Woodman
Zoe Woods
J L Yates

SHIT MATTER NUTS
BANANAS TOUCHED TAPPED
NOT RIGHT UP TOP OFF YOUR ROCKE
SCREW LOOSE
NUTJO BARMY
FRUITCAKE
LOOPY
CRACKERS
DONKERS WACKO STARK RAVIN
ST THE PLOT DO LALLY
LOONY CUCKOO

First published in 2020

Unbound
6th Floor Mutual House, 70 Conduit Street, London W1S 2GF
www.unbound.com

Text and art design by Lucy Sullivan

Barking Font design by Dan Berry

Edited by Lizzie Kaye

Supported using public funding by the National Lottery through Arts Council England

Supported using public funding by
**ARTS COUNCIL
ENGLAND**

Supported by the Lakes International Comics Arts Festival

A CIP record for this book is available from the British Library

ISBN 978-1-78352-880-6 (hardback)
ISBN 978-1-78352-881-3 (ebook)

Printed in the U.K by Comic Printing UK

1 2 3 4 5 6 7 8 9